TRINITY GUILDHALL

Drum Kit 1

Pieces & Studies
for Trinity Guildhall examinations
2011–2013

Grades 1 & 2

Published by
Trinity College London
89 Albert Embankment
London SE1 7TP UK

T +44 (0)20 7820 6100
F +44 (0)20 7820 6161
E music@trinityguildhall.co.uk
www.trinityguildhall.co.uk

Trinity Guildhall graded drum kit examinations

Introduction

The role of the drum kit player is a multifaceted one; drummers are required to play a multitude of styles (and often instruments) with conviction, flair and musical confidence. In show and cabaret playing, drummers are also required to have the ability to read and improvise. Stylistic versatility is essential to a drum kit player: the Latin American and African rhythms that are becoming increasingly influential and popular in contemporary music, strict tempo ballroom styles, contemporary pop and rock, not to mention jazz and funk, all need to be assessed. The strength of the Trinity Guildhall drum kit syllabus lies in not only challenging candidates, but in developing them towards becoming accomplished musicians.

In today's performing arena, drum kit playing is 90% accompaniment and 10% solo. It is therefore the aim of the Trinity Guildhall examination system to reflect this and to cover as broad a style base as possible over the eight grades.

Rudiment playing is assessed in a stylistic way, with candidates performing rudimental studies pertinent to the instrument. Rudiments are presented progressively for each grade and stylistic studies are performed as separate musical entities alongside the pieces.

Drum kit examinations

Candidates are required to perform:

- a rudimental study (or studies)
- one piece from Group A (played with a backing track)
- one piece from Group B (unaccompanied)
- two supporting tests

Please refer to the current syllabus for details of supporting tests.

Rudimental studies are specially written pieces that involve all the rudiments set for a particular grade (see cumulative rudiments grid). These rudiments are set out at the beginning of each grade section. Candidates will be required to learn these in order to be able to play the study (or studies).

Group A pieces have full backing accompaniment on CD with click track where appropriate, but no drums. Candidates will be marked on their ability to interpret a typical drum chart and interact with the backing in terms of time-keeping, phrasing, soloing etc.

Group B pieces are unaccompanied.

Venue equipment

At Public Centres where percussion examinations are accepted, Trinity Guildhall will normally supply a good quality five-piece drum kit that comprises:

- snare drum with adjustable drum kit (not orchestral) stand
- bass drum (18-22")
- ride cymbal (18-22")
- splash for Grades 5-8
- 3 toms (minimum) high/medium/low
- hi hat (12-14")
- crash cymbal (14-18")
- adjustable drum stool

In the case of an Examiner Visit, the visit organiser is responsible for providing the drum kit.

Drum heads should be in good condition and tuned correctly, and all stands and pedals should be in good mechanical order. Larger kits may be used, as may flat drum kits, but electric drum kits may not. Double bass drum pedals may be used in solos and fills if desired. Candidates wishing to use their own kits may only do so at the discretion of the Centre Representative, and the setting up of the kit must not be allowed to interfere with the timing of the session.

In all cases candidates must provide their own sticks, which must be in good condition and suitable for the repertoire being performed. When the examination entry is made, it should be clearly indicated on the entry form if a drum kit candidate is left handed.

For all drum kit grades it is the responsibility of the person signing the entry form to ensure that suitable playback equipment for CDs is provided. Some centres may provide this equipment and the applicant should contact the centre well in advance to confirm the arrangements. In all cases, arrangements (about power supply, equipment insurance etc.) must be agreed with the Centre Representative.

The equipment must be of good quality, comprising CD player with track search facility and good quality loudspeakers that are capable of reproducing the volume required for comfortable playalong (c. 20W). 'Ghetto blasters' are to be discouraged unless they have sufficient power to enable comfortable monitoring of CD for playalong or are connected to an external amplifier. Headphones may be worn by the candidate as long as there is a separate amplification route that enables the examiner to hear both drum kit and backing adequately.

Please note that a percussion-equipped warm-up room is not supplied for percussion examinations.

Trinity Guildhall recommends the use of ear defenders by candidates and examiners for the performance of drum kit repertoire for health and safety reasons. These should be used for all pieces and studies.

Drum kit rudiments

Rudiment	Grade 1	Grade 2	Grade 3	Grade 4	Grade 5	Grade 6	Grade 7	Grade 8
Single strokes	✓	✓	✓	✓	✓	✓	✓	✓
Double strokes	✓	✓	✓	✓	✓	✓	✓	✓
Single paradiddle	✓	✓	✓	✓	✓	✓	✓	✓
Flam		✓	✓	✓	✓	✓	✓	✓
Drag		✓	✓	✓	✓	✓	✓	✓
Four stroke ruff		✓	✓	✓	✓	✓	✓	✓
Five stroke roll			✓	✓	✓	✓	✓	✓
Seven stroke roll			✓	✓	✓	✓	✓	✓
Nine stroke roll			✓	✓	✓	✓	✓	✓
Flam tap				✓	✓	✓	✓	✓
Flam accent				✓	✓	✓	✓	✓
Flamacue				✓	✓	✓	✓	✓
Flam paradiddle				✓	✓	✓	✓	✓
Double paradiddle				✓	✓	✓	✓	✓
Paradiddle-diddle				✓	✓	✓	✓	✓
Drag and stroke					✓	✓	✓	✓
Double drag and stroke					✓	✓	✓	✓
Drag paradiddle					✓	✓	✓	✓
Single ratamacue					✓	✓	✓	✓
Double ratamacue					✓	✓	✓	✓
Triple ratamacue					✓	✓	✓	✓
Triple paradiddle						✓	✓	✓
Reverse paradiddle						✓	✓	✓
Pata fla fla							✓	✓
Swiss army triplet							✓	✓
Inward paradiddle							✓	✓

Drum kit notation key

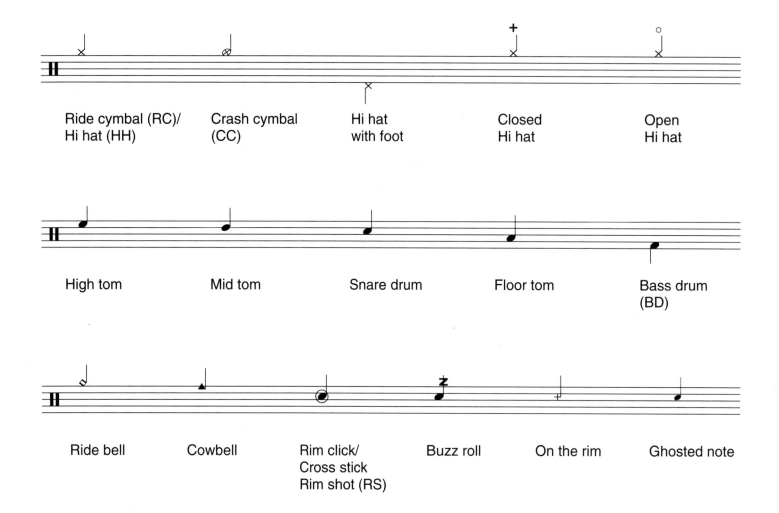

Ride cymbal (RC)/ Hi hat (HH)   Crash cymbal (CC)   Hi hat with foot   Closed Hi hat   Open Hi hat

High tom   Mid tom   Snare drum   Floor tom   Bass drum (BD)

Ride bell   Cowbell   Rim click/ Cross stick Rim shot (RS)   Buzz roll   On the rim   Ghosted note

Performance notes

General note for both grades

Where a crash cymbal appears at the start of a bar and is followed by one-bar repeat signs (⊞ⅈⅈ⊞), the crash cymbal should **not** be played in the repeat bars. This is universally accepted as standard drum kit notation and it is the aim of the Trinity Guildhall syllabus to encourage students to become familiar with what they will be confronted with in the real world of drum kit performance.

All repeats, including those within *da capo* and *dal segno* sections, should be observed in drum kit examinations.

Grade 1

Dave Webster   Grade 1 Rudimental Study

A straight 8s solo presenting the Grade 1 rudiments on the full kit.

Malcolm Ball   Jack in the Box

A straight 8s feel against some syncopated backing phrases.

Andrew Tween/
Jonathan Taylor Chicano

The track starts with a steady rock beat in the A section leading to a Latin groove in the B section (bars 9–17). It is important to keep a steady count throughout the piece, especially in the unison section in bars 18–20 – keep your time steady with the click so you don't fall behind or push ahead.

The name *Chicano* comes from the crossover of Rock and Latin music, notably from people of Mexican descent, although it could cover any Latin American rock style. Typical musical examples of this would be Santana or Los Lobos.

Pete Riley/
Andy Staples   Zigfunk

Based around a funk sound similar to that of New Orleans band The Meters, *Zigfunk* features a quaver-/eighth-note-based feel throughout. During the A and C sections this is played on the hi hat with occasional additional snare drum notes for punctuation, while the B section features a brief excursion onto the ride cymbal. The most challenging part is left to the end at section D, where the drum fills use single stroke semiquavers/sixteenth notes. Finally, be sure to choke the last cymbal crash to create a tight ending with the track.

Luke Wastell   Monkey March

Standard march-style piece in $\frac{2}{4}$ time. Performance of this piece should convey a solid sense of time and understanding of military band marches.

Stevie Smith   Sunny Side Up

This piece has a basic multi-purpose Latin groove and should be performed in a light and controlled way. Letter A has a *baion* feel and letter B gives the opportunity to improvise solo fills.

Rick Hudson   Top Hat

A piece in $\frac{3}{4}$ time that develops coordination between hands and feet.

Grade 2

Dave Webster — Grade 2 Rudimental Study

All flams, drags and ruffs are to be played using alternate sticking. Use single stroke roll sticking in bars 2 and 4, double stroke roll sticking in bar 6, and paradiddle sticking in bars 9 and 10. The ruffs in bars 7, 8, 13 and 14 can be played starting on the beat or alternatively on the 'and' of the previous beat.

George Double — Feels Good

This is a light groove for four-piece kit. Listen to the ensemble, in particular the bass line, and let the kit part sit steadily with the track. Aim for a well-rounded tone from the drums, but do not go beyond the directed mf – let the melody come through.

Ben Beer — Down on the Floor

This piece has an alternative rock feel with fills around the kit.

Malcolm Ball — Soft Cheese

Keep a relaxed groove but tight with the backing. Listen hard in the final two bars to get used to playing the **rit.** with the backing.

Ralph Salmins — Capricorn March

This is a funky march incorporating rudiments. Stay relaxed and try to maintain a strong march feel throughout. It is important to keep the notes as even and in time as possible while making the most of the dynamics. The rolls in bars 1, 2, 43 and 44 can be played either as double stroke or multiple bounce rolls.

Keith Bartlett — Fill Drill

This piece should sparkle from start to finish and gives the perfect opportunity to show off your rock drumming skills. Take note of the dynamics and really play up the accents in bars 13-20. Keep a lively but steady tempo throughout, and make sure you don't rush towards the end as the piece increases in excitement!

Neil Robinson — Cleverstix

A melodic solo introducing some off-beat quaver/eighth-note rhythms and use of the hi hat with foot. At bar 4 use tom rim for the click sound. Bars 17-22 should have a solid half-time feel.

Grade 1 Rudiments

You will need to learn these rudiments to be able to play the Grade 1 Rudimental Study.

Single strokes

Double strokes

Single paradiddle

If you are left handed you may reverse the sticking.

Grade 1 Rudimental Study

Dave Webster

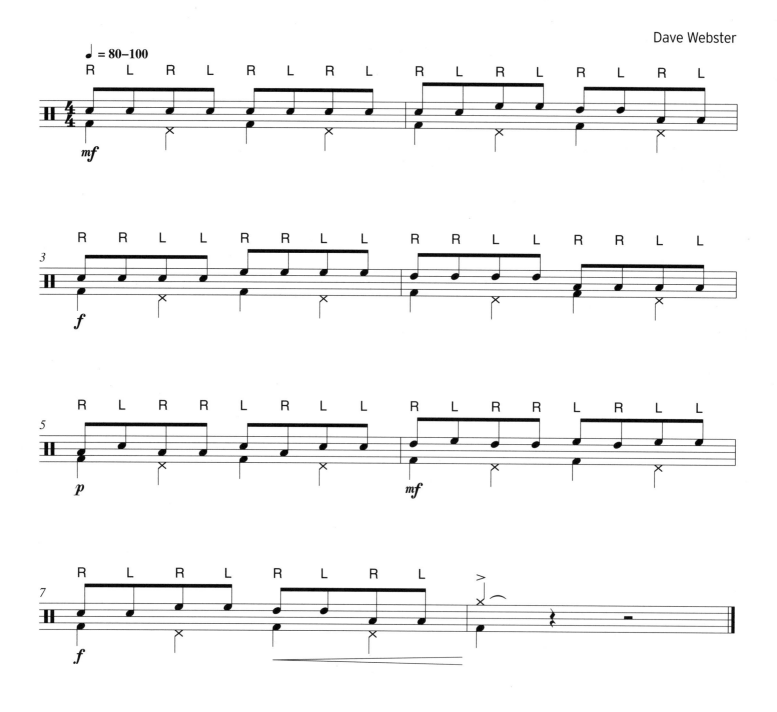

Remember to look at the Performance Notes on pages 5-6

Jack in the Box

Malcolm Ball

Remember to look at the Performance Notes on pages 5-6

Chicano

Andrew Tween/Jonathan Taylor

φ = Half-open Trashy HH.

Remember to look at the Performance Notes on pages 5-6

Zigfunk

Pete Riley/Andy Staples

Play with dynamics appropriate to the music.

Remember to look at the Performance Notes on pages 5-6

Monkey March

Luke Wastell

Remember to look at the Performance Notes on pages 5-6

Sunny Side Up

Stevie Smith

Remember to look at the Performance Notes on pages 5-6

Top Hat

Rick Hudson

Remember to look at the Performance Notes on pages 5-6

Grade 2 Rudiments

You will need to learn the following to be able to play the Grade 2 Rudimental Study.

Single strokes

Double strokes

Single paradiddle

please turn over

Flams

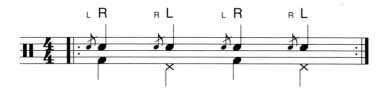

Drags

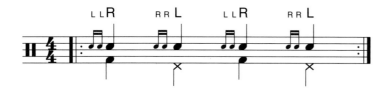

Four stroke ruffs

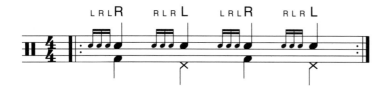

Grade 2 Rudimental Study

Dave Webster

Remember to look at the Performance Notes on pages 5-6

Feels Good

George Double

Remember to look at the Performance Notes on pages 5-6

Down on the Floor

Ben Beer

Remember to look at the Performance Notes on pages 5-6

Soft Cheese

Malcolm Ball

Remember to look at the Performance Notes on pages 5-6

Capricorn March

Ralph Salmins

Remember to look at the Performance Notes on pages 5-6

Fill Drill

Keith Bartlett

Remember to look at the Performance Notes on pages 5-6

Cleverstix

Neil Robinson

* These notes can be played on any tom.

Remember to look at the Performance Notes on pages 5-6